SMALL POND

New York: E. P. Dutton & Co., Inc.

SMALL POND

by Marguerite Walters

wood engravings by Stefan Martin

To the children who lived in the nearest house

Spring

The first warm sun, like magic, touched the pond awake. It melted icy slivers around the little pond's edge. It started peepers peeping, loud at the end of the day.

The children who lived in the nearest house heard the shrill frog song.

"The pond's awake," the children whispered. "Listen! The pond's awake."

Each day the sun shone warmer down on the little pond.

The frogs and all their cousins came out of their winter beds. Their eyes were bright and shining as they sat around the pond. In the shallow water they laid their many eggs. Soon, quick little long-tailed tadpoles swam among the weeds.

Up from the muddy bottom, lily plants pushed toward the light. Pussy willows grew along the shore. Their tiny silvery catkins were soft as a kitten's coat.

Busily in the willows, songbirds built their nests,
stopping now and then to sing the happiest songs
they knew.

Sometimes, as the sun went down, a deer came there to drink. Prints of his sharp little hoofs were deep in the soft brown earth.

11

Summer

Each day the sun shone warmer.

Water grass grew tall.

Pussy willow catkins grew powdery and long.

Baby birds, too big for their nests, tried their wings and flew.

Tadpoles
turning into
frogs, grew their
jumping legs and
jumped.

Water lilies opened. The lovely flowers floated there, smelling very sweet. The children picked a few that grew closest to the shore. The flat green lily pads were rafts for tiny frogs to rest on.

15

Turtles sunned themselves on rocks, then dived down into the water.

Dragonflies climbed the water grass and dried their beautiful wings. They hovered over the water like jewels in the light. Suddenly they darted, looking for something to eat.

All summer the sun shone brightly, with time out for summer rain.

Birds took time from singing to flutter down and bathe.

The children splashed like turtles. They swam like little frogs. And they laughed at the tiny fishes that tickled their wiggling toes.

Fall

After the brightest of summer's days, the sun was no longer so warm.

Rain fell cooler. Wind blew colder.

Days grew shorter again.

Green leaves turned to yellow and red. They fell on the little pond. They blew like elfin sailboats, driven before the wind.

The children who lived in the nearest house watched the leaves blow and go.

They looked into last spring's bird
nests. No little birds were there.

They listened for happy songs, but
the singing birds had flown.

They watched for the darting dragonflies. Not a dragonfly was in sight.

"Where are the sweet-smelling lilies?" they asked.

The lily plants were under the water.

They searched for frogs and turtles.

"And where are the toads?" they wondered.

But the frogs and turtles and toads were down in the earth, tucked well away from the cold.

All day the pond was very still. But sometimes in the night, wild ducks, and even the great wild geese, stopped to rest there in their flight.

Then, from their windows, the children heard the sound of many wings rising from the darkened pond and flying away toward the south. The honking call of the geese in the sky was like the sound of flying bells.

Winter

At last the days grew shortest of all. Under the cold gray sky, the freezing touch of winter turned the pond to shining ice.

Then the children who lived in the nearest house ran to the pond with skates. They glided around and all across it. They whirled like the wind upon it.

One day, one child said, "Listen!"

They stopped. Not one stirred or said a word.

In the silence, snow came sifting. It whispered down through the last dry leaves.

It fell on the children's caps and on their eye-lashes. It fell on their mittens and shoes.

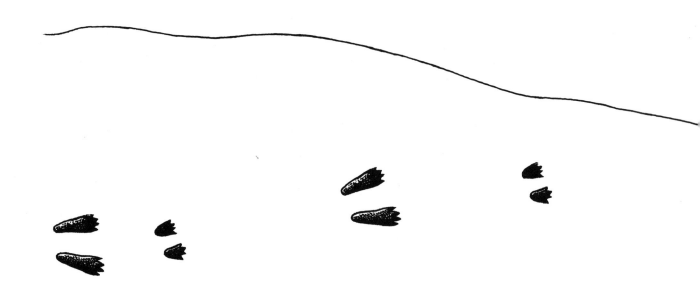

Softly all night, snow, falling, covered the little pond. The winter-morning sunlight showed nothing there but white, crossed by a pattern of footprints, where a fox and a scampering rabbit had traced their way across it.

The little pond lay hidden deeply under the snow.

31

But after the coldest winter, days always grow warmer again. Soon the bright spring sun, like magic, touches the pond awake. It melts the icy slivers around the little pond's edge. It starts the peepers peeping, loud at the end of day.

Then the children who live in the nearest house hear the shrill frog song once more.

"Listen," they whisper from their windows at night.

"Listen! The pond's awake."